Surf's Up

Contents

The Dawn of Surfing

Written by Phillip Moore

Surfing began more than 1600 years ago.
Songs and stories about people surfing waves
on boards first came from Hawaii. Some stories
told how the people used the big surf waves to
bring in the boats full of fish.

Surfing in Hawaii

For hundreds of years the Hawaiian people
did not write down their songs and stories.
Older people told the children
about special things that went on.
Some of the songs and stories
told about people surfing on boards.

Did you know
that people were
surfing in Hawaii before
Christopher Columbus
discovered America?

The early Hawaiians had laws,
which were known as *kapu*.
Some kapu were about surfing.
Kapu said that the noblemen,
who the Hawaiians call *ali'i*,
had to surf at some beaches
and the rest of the people
had to surf at other beaches.
Kapu also said that the noblemen
had to have bigger surfboards than
the rest of the people!

Making the First Surfboards

The early Hawaiians used the wood
of special trees to make their surfboards.
Surfboard makers used a tool called an adze
to cut a tree trunk into the shape
of a surfboard. The noblemen's surfboards
had to be 14 to 16 feet (4.27 to 4.88 m) long.
The rest of the people's surfboards had to be
10 to 12 feet (3 to 3.65 m) long.
The Hawaiians used coral and rough stones
to make the boards smooth. Then they rubbed
the surfboards with roots and bark to make
the boards shiny and black.

**How long
do you think it
took to make a
surfboard?**

Surfing Ceremonies

The early Hawaiians had many ceremonies. Some of these ceremonies were about surfing. The first surfing ceremony was when the tree was chosen for the board. A red fish called *kumu* was put under the tree. When the tree was cut down, the fish was put into a hole near the roots of the tree. There were special chants for this ceremony. When the surfboard was ready, another ceremony took place before the surfboard was put into the ocean.

How Surfing Spread

In the last one hundred years,
other people in Hawaii have started surfing.
One of the best surfers was an Irish-Hawaiian
boy named George Freeth.

In 1907, George Freeth left Hawaii and
went to California to show the people there
how to surf. George Freeth stayed in California
and became their first surf lifeguard.
He became a hero when he made three trips
through big surf in a storm to save
seven Japanese fishermen.

Then lots of people all around the world
took up surfing. People now ride the waves in
places as far north as Iceland and
as far south as New Zealand.

Back to the Surf

Written by Dean Iversen
Illustrated by Mark Wilson

This weekend would be the first time
that my brother Dave and I
had been back to the surf club
since the accident two years ago.

We both love the sea. After surfing all day,
Dave and I had spent many nights
talking about the waves that we'd caught.
We had some great times!

Dave had learned to surf in just one day!
After a week, he was surfing better than most people.
But that was the same with most things Dave did.

I was surprised when Dave said
we should go to the surfing contest this year.
I was even more surprised
when he took my surfboard out from the garage
and tied it onto the car.
I hadn't surfed since Dave's accident.
It just wouldn't have seemed right.
Surfing was what we had always done together.
I didn't want to do it without him.

It was dark when we got to the surf club.
We got there two days before the contest.
When we put up the tent, Dave said
we could use his artificial leg for a tent pole.
He often made jokes like that.

We were very tired when we got into our sleeping bags.
All we could hear was the sound of the waves
crashing on the beach.

When I woke up, Dave wasn't there.
Then I saw him outside sitting on the beach,
looking at the waves.
I was about to call him, when he stood up.
He grabbed the big old surfboard
he had taken from the surf club and headed for the sea.

How would
you describe the
relationship between
the two brothers?

I didn't know what to do. Dave was a strong swimmer.
Even with only one leg, he would be safe in the water.
But I was worried about how he would feel if he failed.
The big brother in me wanted to stop him,
but I knew I couldn't. So, I sat down on the beach
to watch.

The first few waves pushed Dave back to the shore.
He was diving under the waves too early
and getting caught in the backwash.
It's hard work getting through the white water.
At last, Dave got his timing right
and got past the breaking waves.

Then he just sat out there on the swells for a long time.
I think he must have been sorting things out in his mind.
Then he turned his board and paddled hard
to catch a wave. I wanted him to do it!
I willed him to surf again! Dave kept paddling.
The wave picked up his board.
Dave pushed up with his arms and jumped onto his feet.
He slipped and fell into the sea. But that was all right,
it was his first try. He started out for the next wave.

The next hour was hard. I watched Dave fall off
wave after wave. It was always the same.
He would stand up and his artificial leg would slip
on the surfboard, and he would fall off.
But he didn't give up. Each time, he got back
on his board and tried again.

My heart began to sink when I saw Dave
slowly paddle back to the beach.
He had tried so hard. I felt so sad for him.
I could tell he was angry when he got to the beach.
He unstrapped his artificial leg and threw it
onto the soft sand. I sank down
and put my head in my hands.

When I looked up, Dave wasn't coming up the beach.
He was paddling out through the waves again.
He didn't try to catch the first two waves,
but turned and paddled for the third one.
As the wave caught him, he pushed up with his arms.
He balanced on his knee and bent his good leg
in front of him. He moved his weight to turn the board,
and he was surfing!

Wow, Dave had done it! I was so proud of him.
I raced to get my board. Dave didn't say much,
but the look on his face said it all.
As we both turned to catch the same wave,
he looked at me and said, "You'd better
stay out of my way. I still can't turn this thing."

Then, he caught the wave and headed for the shore.

Harry and Larry Go Bodysurfing

Written by Reuben Nelson
Illustrated by Fraser Williamson

Harry and Larry are going bodysurfing. Larry gets things right. But Harry wants to do things his own way!

Larry

Harry

I'm going down next to the surf club. Between the flags.

Water looks OK here.

No, Harry. There's a rip here.

Rips

A rip is water that is going out to sea. Rips are made by waves coming into the shore and turning. The water goes along the beach until it finds a way back out to sea.

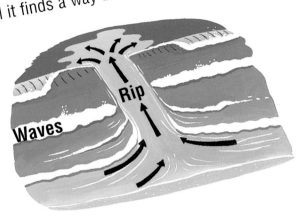

How to Identify a Rip

Look for flat water next to waves. Sometimes there will be seaweed floating out to sea. Near the shore, the water might be muddy and sandy. Sometimes the water is foamy.

No, there isn't. Look, the water's flat.

Later...

Help! Lifeguard!
My friend needs help!
He's getting swept out
to sea!

I can see him.
He's caught in
the rip!

Some Signs that Tell a Lifeguard that Someone Might Need Help

Hair in Eyes
People with hair in their eyes could be struggling to keep their heads above the water.

Waves Washing over Heads
People usually duck under waves when they are going out in the surf. Someone who isn't ducking under the waves might need help.

Waving Hands
Waving in the surf can be a sign that someone needs help.

Head Falling Back
People with their heads back and their faces up might need help.

Bobbing Up and Down
People bobbing up and down in the waves could be struggling to get air.

Lying with Faces Down in the Water
People lying with their faces down in the water might need help!

Why should you always wear sunblock when you are out in the sun?

Here are some ways the lifeguard could get free if Harry grabs the lifeguard instead of the tube.

What if Harry grabs the lifeguard's wrist?

The lifeguard could push his free arm between Harry's arms.
Then the lifeguard would clasp his own hands.
The lifeguard could break Harry's grip by pressing on Harry's thumbs.
The lifeguard could push his own arms down, or up, quickly.

What if Harry grabs the lifeguard's head or neck?

The lifeguard could take a big breath and tuck his chin in close to his chest.
The lifeguard could grab Harry's elbows and push his thumbs into the inside of Harry's elbows.
The lifeguard could push Harry's arms up then slide down under the water to escape.

Grab the tube, Harry.

What training would a lifeguard need?

Research

You can't expect to know everything in life. What is important is that you know where to look to find the answers to any questions you might have. Here are five questions about the sports shown on this page. Make a list of where you might find the answers to these questions.

Questions to start your research

What do you already know about these sports?

What things are the same about these sports?

In what way are any of these sports like – or not like – surfing?

Which of these sports is a mixture of surfing and another sport?

What other questions would you like to have answers to?

Glossary

 **adze** – a hand tool with a steel blade for working timber

 **ali'i** – Hawaiian word for people regarded by the Hawaiians as noblemen

 **artificial leg** – a leg that has been made to replace a leg that has been lost through illness or accident

 **body surfing** – a way of riding a wave without a surfboard

 **coral** – a group of marine animals with skeletons that form rocklike island reefs

 **kapu** – Hawaiian word for the laws of the early Hawaiian people

 **kumu** – a red fish found in Hawaii

 **rip** – a ribbon of flat water among the waves where the water rushes out to sea